D0119821

DOCTOR · WHO

THE OOD

BBC CHILDREN'S BOOKS
Published by the Penguin Group
Penguin Books Ltd, 80 Strand, London, WC2R 0RL, England
Penguin Group (USA), Inc., 375 Hudson Street, New York, New York 10014, USA
Penguin Books (Australia) Ltd, 250 Camberwell Road, Camberwell, Victoria 3124, Australia.
(A division of Pearson Australia Group Pty Ltd)
Canada, India, New Zealand, South Africa.
Published by BBC Children's Books, 2008

Written by Moray Laing. Disappearing Act by Justin Richards.
10 9 8 7 6 5 4 3 2 1

Printed in China.
ISBN-13: 978-1-40590-0442-1
ISBN-10: 1-40590-442-9

CONTENTS

Meet the Ood

Introduction....4
Ood Data....6
Ood Anatomy....8
⬢ Test your knowledge

Oodkind

Ood....10
Natural Ood....11
Ood Sigma....12
The Ood Brain....13
⬢ Test your knowledge

Ood Friends and Enemies

The Doctor, Rose, Donna....14
Sanctuary Base Six....15
The Beast....15
Klineman Halpen....16
Friends of the Ood....16
⬢ Test your knowledge

Background

Ood-Sphere....18
Krop Tor....19
Red-Eye....20
Telepathy....20
The Circle....21
⬢ Test your knowledge

Converting the Ood

Ood Conversion....22
Ood Operations....23
Translator Ball....24
Warehouse Fifteen....24
⬢ Test your knowledge

Ood Encounters

On Krop Tor....26
On the Planet of the Ood....28
⬢ Test your knowledge

Test your knowledge Answers....30

Disappearing Act....31

4 MEET THE OOD

In the 42nd century, the Second Great and Bountiful Human Empire spans three galaxies, and the Ood live only to serve people.

At first glance, the Ood look quite terrifying. They have fleshy tentacles in place of a nose and mouth. However, this race of mildly telepathic creatures is completely harmless, unless they become infected.

Humans believe that all Ood want to do is serve people. By the year 4126, at least fifty per cent of all homes across Galactic Central have an Ood to carry out all their menial tasks. Most people don't think it's cruel to own an Ood because if they don't receive any orders the creatures just pine and eventually die.

The Ood don't have individual names, just numbers, but humans like to think of Ood as trusted friends. Unfortunately, the problem with the Ood is that, being telepathic, they are prone to being taken over by creatures with stronger minds. And that's when the trouble begins.

Name: Ood

Species: Oodkind

Height: 1.83m (6ft)

Home Planet: Ood-Sphere in the Horsehead Nebula

Skin: Pale, with fleshy red tentacles

Weapons: Translator ball can electrocute victims

Strengths: They do the jobs humans love to hate

Weaknesses: When given no orders, they die

Look out for: Red-Eyed Ood – they're dangerous!

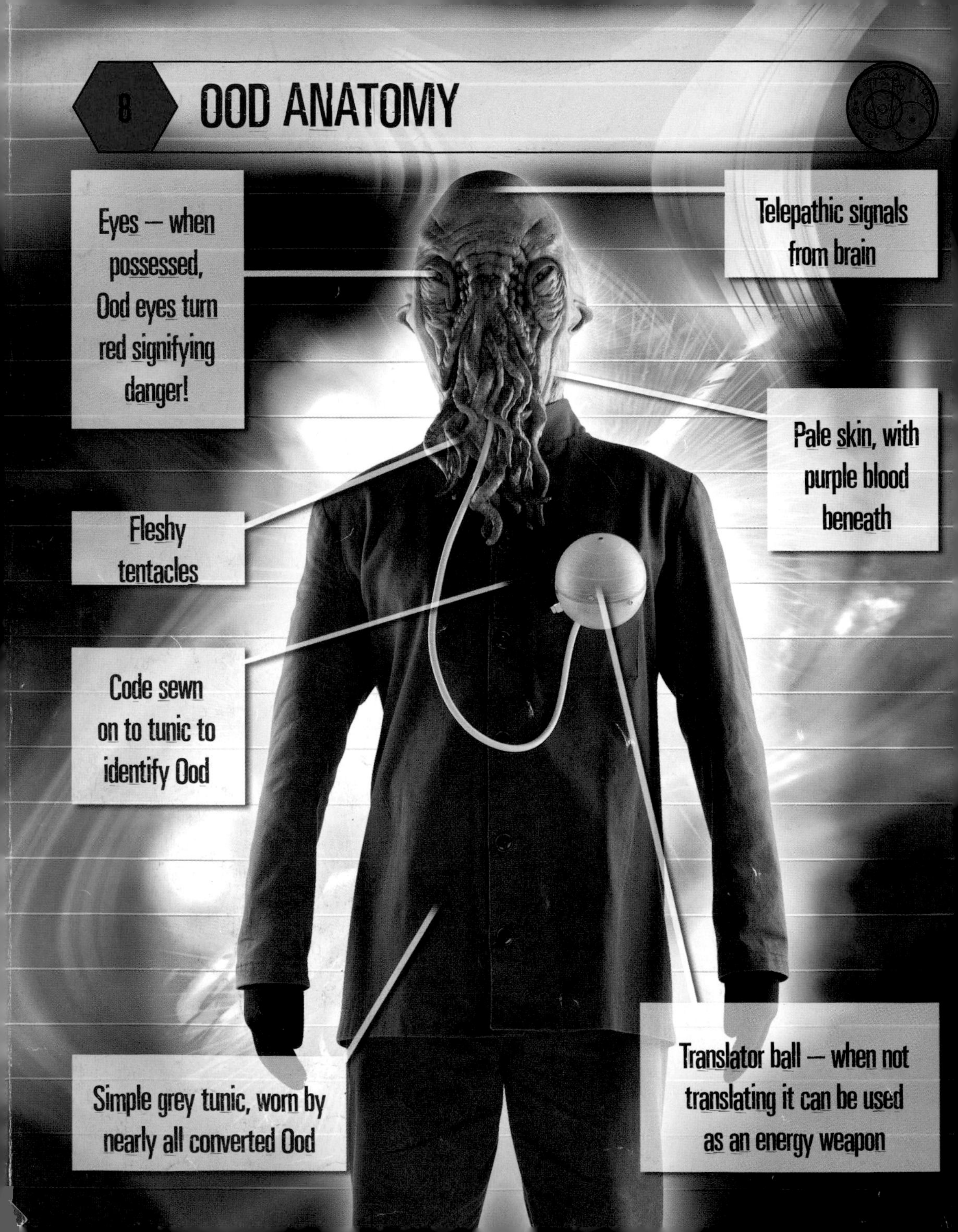
8
OOD ANATOMY
Eyes — when possessed, Ood eyes turn red signifying danger!
Telepathic signals from brain
Pale skin, with purple blood beneath
Fleshy tentacles
Code sewn on to tunic to identify Ood
Simple grey tunic, worn by nearly all converted Ood
Translator ball — when not translating it can be used as an energy weapon

TEST YOUR KNOWLEDGE

OODKIND

OOD

Humans don't just breed Ood, they convert them into slaves. Their Hind-Brain is cut off and replaced by a translator ball. In this way, a workforce of Ood who want to serve is created.

Ood come with a standard translator setting, but can be adapted to a variety of different styles, including one with a female voice or a comedy classic setting for humour. Ood are used across the galaxy as servants to carry out all the jobs humans don't want to do. They are considered better than robots because they don't need technical support or software upgrades. An Ood is for life.

NATURAL OOD

In their natural state, Ood used to roam around happily on the ice plains of the Ood-Sphere. Natural Ood sing to each other telepathically, and the songs are beautiful. They are quite different from the processed Ood that end up serving humans.

Born with a Hind-Brain that contains their memories and emotions, they hold it out in front of them in their hands like some kind of offering. Donna thought that a creature born with a brain in its hands would have to trust anyone it meets.

OOD SIGMA

Ood Sigma is the personal assistant to Halpen, the Chief Executive of Ood Operations on the Ood's home planet. Ood Sigma wears a special grey suit with a Greek Sigma on the pocket. Halpen thinks of him as his faithful servant, but Ood Sigma is secretly turning the power-hungry Chief Exec into Oodkind, with the fake hair tonic in his hip flask.

THE OOD BRAIN

Centuries before Ood Operations started processing Ood, the Ood Brain was found beneath the Northern Glacier on the Ood-Sphere. The brain is the telepathic centre of Oodkind and connects the creatures with a beautiful song.

An Ood is unable to survive with a separate forebrain and Hind-Brain because they would constantly be at war with themselves, so the Ood Brain brings them together. A massive pulsating brain, the captured Ood Brain fills an entire warehouse on the Ood-Sphere. Oodkind needs the Ood Brain to survive – if it dies, so do the Ood creatures.

TEST YOUR KNOWLEDGE

OOD FRIENDS AND ENEMIES

THE DOCTOR, ROSE AND DONNA

The Doctor, along with his friend Rose Tyler, first met the Ood when the TARDIS landed inside Sanctuary Base Six on the planet Krop Tor. Initially the time travellers thought that the Ood wanted to eat them, but the Ood translator balls were faulty and the Ood were really offering them food instead!

The Ood-Sphere was the first alien planet that the Doctor took Donna Noble to. Donna's first encounter with an Ood was with Ood Delta Fifty, who was dying in the snow. Donna, like Rose, soon realised that the Ood are not really willing servants to humankind at all – they are no more than slaves – and she was appalled at their treatment.

SANCTUARY BASE SIX

The small human crew of Sanctuary Base Six on Krop Tor used a group of fifty Ood to help them drill down into the depths of the planet, as well as cooking and looking after them. Their computer didn't even register Ood as proper life forms. When a hidden creature called the Beast awoke, the Ood were taken over by him and suddenly became his legion. They attempted to kill the crew one by one.

THE BEAST

Chained deep beneath the planet Krop Tor, the Disciples of Light had enslaved the massive Beast millions of years ago. The creature possessed one of the crew, Toby Zed, and then used the Ood in his attempt to escape from the pit. When possessed by the Beast, the Ood's eyes glowed bright red.

KLINEMAN HALPEN

Klineman Halpen was the Chief Executive of Ood Operations on the Ood-Sphere. When sales of Ood began to slow, Halpen reduced the price to fifty credits and expected the Ood conversion to be doubled. Halpen's father took him to the warehouse containing the Ood Brain when he was only six years old, and he always knew the horrific truth about how the Natural Ood were converted into slaves. Halpen believed the Doctor and Donna to be Friends of the Ood activists and was eventually turned into an Ood himself by Ood Sigma.

FRIENDS OF THE OOD

The Friends of the Ood, or FOTO, a group of people who think that Ood are treated badly and should be free. Head of Ood Management, Doctor Ryder, secretly worked for FOTO. It took him ten years to get inside Ood Operations. When he did, he was able to lower the barrier that prevented the Ood from connecting with each other, allowing some of the Ood to break free. This eventually brought about the destruction of Ood Operations, although Ryder was killed by Halpen in the process.

TEST YOUR KNOWLEDGE

OOD-SPHERE

A planet in the Horsehead Nebula, the distant world of Ood-Sphere is a cold, windswept place with ice plains covered in snow. This breathtaking world is the home planet of the Ood and the Ood Brain. The Doctor visited this solar system years ago, when he landed on the nearby planet Sense-Sphere.

KROP TOR

Krop Tor, meaning 'the bitter pill', is impossibly situated next to a powerful black hole. A small group of fifty Ood worked for the crew of Sanctuary Base Six. The creatures became possessed by the Beast that was imprisoned in a pit deep in the heart of the planet. All the Ood on Krop Tor were killed when the planet eventually fell into the black hole.

RED-EYE

An immediate warning that an Ood has become infected and is dangerous is when it develops something called Red-Eye. When the creatures' eyes glow bright red, the Ood become uncharacteristically savage, will disobey orders and may even attempt to kill.

On Krop Tor, this was a sign that the Beast had possessed them. When the Doctor and Donna met them on the Ood-Sphere, it showed that the Ood were trying to finally break free.

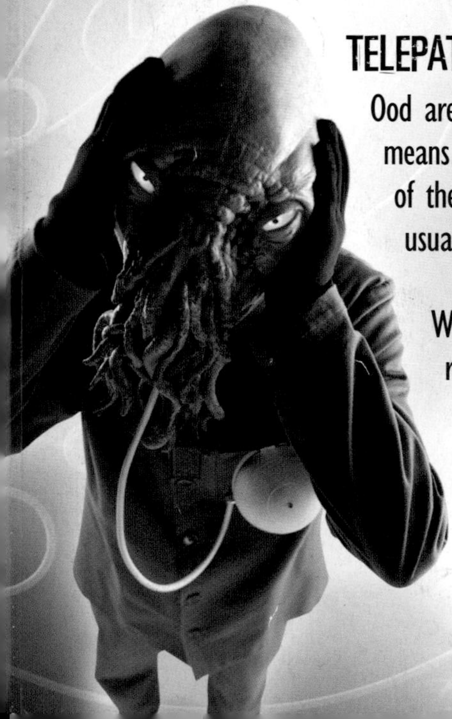

TELEPATHY

Ood are able to communicate with each other telepathically, which means they can hear each other in their minds. On Krop Tor, one of the crew, Danny Bartok, monitored their telepathic field. It was usually rated at Basic 5.

When the Ood were disturbed by the Beast the telepathic field rose to Basic 30, which was the equivalent of them screaming and shouting silently inside their heads, and it eventually rose to Basic 100. Danny thought this was impossible, as technically it meant they should have been dead.

Danny eventually managed to send out a telepathic flare to Basic Zero, which caused the possessed Ood to collapse.

THE CIRCLE

When the Doctor and Donna met a dying Ood on the ice plains of the Ood's home planet, the creature said that 'the circle must be broken'. Later, when Donna was trapped with Red-Eyed Ood they mentioned that the circle must be broken so that they could sing.

The circle literally referred to the pylons surrounding the Ood Brain, which dampened the telepathic field. When the circle was finally broken, the Ood could communicate with each other freely again. Oodkind contacted each other across the galaxy requesting that the Ood all come home – as they were free at last.

TEST YOUR KNOWLEDGE

CONVERTING THE OOD

OOD CONVERSION

The Doctor thought that a species born to serve could never evolve. He realised that Ood Operations was doing something to create creatures with no concept of freedom and a desire to obey.

He soon discovered the horrible truth – Ood Operations was ripping out the Ood's Hind-Brain and then replacing it with a translator ball to create the perfect servant.

OOD OPERATIONS

Based on the Ood-Sphere, Ood Operations, also known affectionately as Double O, was the main headquarters for the conversion of Natural Ood into Oodkind ready to be sold. Converted Ood were kept in containers, ready to be flown out by rocket to the three galaxies.

Ood Operations were looking to expand into new territories before the Ood managed to break the circle and Ood Operations was closed down.

TRANSLATOR BALL

All the converted Ood carry a white orb in front of them, in place of where they would normally carry their Hind-Brain. This white ball is used as a translating device so that they can communicate with humans.

The ball lights up when an Ood is talking and can be clipped on to their tunic when not in use.

When an Ood is infected, this white ball can be used as a lethal weapon. One touch from the translator ball can zap the victim with energy – and kill them instantly.

TEST YOUR KNOWLEDGE

WAREHOUSE FIFTEEN

One of the giant warehouses belonging to Ood Operations was called Warehouse Fifteen. Inside this warehouse Ood Operations kept the gigantic pulsating Ood Brain captive. Using a circle of pylons around the creature, the company was able to stop the Ood from communicating with each other and have complete control over them.

OOD ENCOUNTERS

ON KROP TOR

There was a group of fifty Ood serving the humans on Krop Tor, a planet that was impossibly orbiting a black hole.

These Ood were just innocent creatures, unprepared for what happened to them. Their daily routine involved serving the small crew on Sanctuary Base Six and responding to their every command. They cooked, they maintained the base and they even helped to mine – basically they worked as slaves. The crew relied on the creatures, like so many humans across the galaxy. And because Ood pine and die if not given orders, the crew didn't think there was anything wrong in using the Ood to do everything for them.

Drilling down deep into the planet disturbed a massive creature known as the Beast. This horrific monster interfered with the Ood's telepathic field so that he could control them and use them to help him escape his prison.

One of the Ood told Rose that 'The Beast and his armies shall rise from the pit to make war against God.' Immediately it corrected itself and said that it hoped she would enjoy her meal.

Later, with the Doctor trapped in the pit deep beneath the planet, Rose was left on the base to join the crew in the fight against the infected Ood. The possessed Ood attacked the crew and even killed some of them using their translator balls as weapons. Eventually Danny Bartok was able to send out a telepathic flare which made the Ood collapse and stopped them attacking. Krop Tor, along with all the Ood, was destroyed when it was sucked into the black hole.

The crew who escaped recorded the Ood deaths in a final report, awarding them honours for their services.

ON THE PLANET OF THE OOD

After she was reunited with the Doctor, Donna's first intergalactic trip was to the home planet of the Ood, a snowy planet in the Horsehead Nebula called the Ood-Sphere.

On this planet, the Doctor discovered the real reason behind the Ood's willingness to serve humans. It wasn't instinct that made them serve at all – they were being turned into slaves and were part of a profitable business. For many years, Ood Operations had been converting the creatures to sell across three galaxies. An operation removed the Ood's Hind-Brain and added a translator ball in its place.

Unknown to the Chief Executive of Ood Operations, Friends of the Ood had managed to infiltrate the company and help the Ood from the inside.

Although he died saving Oodkind, Doctor Ryder had managed to release the minds of some of the Ood so they could talk to each other telepathically and break free.

With help from the Doctor and Donna Oodkind had been set free. The beautiful song of the freed Ood called enslaved Ood across the galaxy back to their home. As the Doctor and Donna left in the TARDIS, the Ood said that they would never forget them.

TEST YOUR KNOWLEDGE

ANSWERS

Meet the Ood
1 (c) 2 (b) 3 (a) 4 (b) 5 (b)

Oodkind
1 (c) 2 (b) 3 (b) 4 (a) 5 (c)

Ood Friends and Enemies
1 (c) 2 (a) 3 (b) 4 (c) 5 (c)

Background
1 (c) 2 (b) 3 (b) 4 (c) 5 (a)

Converting the Ood
1 (b) 2 (c) 3 (c) 4 (c) 5 (a)

Ood Encounters
1 (c) 2 (b) 3 (a) 4 (c) 5 (b)

DISAPPEARING ACT

Like all the best conjuring acts, it was all a trick. But not the sort of trick that anyone would ever guess or unravel. What people saw when Fergus Antelect performed was quite simply impossible. It was magic.

Tonight Antelect was performing at the Galactic Royal Hotel. He only performed at hotels these days – the larger and more upmarket the better. The richer the audience, the more Antelect expected to make. The more he expected to steal.

Agent Ratner would be in the audience again tonight, Antelect was sure of it. And again Ratner wouldn't see what happened right under his nose. It made Antelect smile to think of how the Special Agent would watch the theft he was there to prevent, and then after the show Ratner himself would provide Antelect with the perfect alibi.

If only Ood Delta wasn't so stupid, the creature could have worked the act itself. But then it was a slave, and Antelect was

its owner. And of course it was all Antelect's idea, all Antelect's money when he sold the jewellery and valuables he took. It was the strength of Antelect's imagination that made it work. Ood Delta was just a means to an end, a way of focusing that imagination telepathically on the audience.

Five minutes till he was on. Antelect checked his appearance in the mirror. Ood Delta should have everything set up by now.

'Water!' he shouted. 'Delta – get me some water. Now, if it isn't too much trouble.'

Ood Delta was there in a moment with a glass of water. Antelect took it, slapping the Ood's hand away.

'Ah – that's tepid,' he snapped. 'You know I like it ice cold. Ice cold.' He dropped the glass and watched it shatter on the expensive marble floor. Water splashed across his shoes.

'Now look what you made me do. Clear that up at once.'

'Of course, Mr Antelect,' Ood Delta said calmly. The fronds

where its mouth should be wobbled as it hooked its translator sphere to its tunic and bent to pick up the fragments of glass.

'And you'd better not be late for the performance,' Antelect said, giving the Ood a kick to get it moving.

'Yes, Mr Antelect,' the creature replied.

The huge ballroom was filled with small round tables where couples and groups of four sat and ate expensive food, while drinking even more expensive wine.

At the end of the ballroom, a stage had been set up, and it was here that Antelect stood. He beamed at the audience, and bowed. Beside him Ood Delta stood silently beside the table of props and equipment that Antelect would use.

Yes, Antelect thought – there was Agent Ratner, sitting near the front, watching closely. He was a big man with a heavy black beard. He was sitting alone, his food untouched in front of him.

Antelect was about to launch into his opening speech when a couple made their noisy way through the ballroom. Why was there always someone who had to arrive late?

The woman was wearing an expensive scarlet dress. Her hair was tied up elaborately, but several strands had escaped and she blew them out of her face. Her partner was tall and slim, wearing his pinstriped suit with casual ease. He followed the woman, apologising quietly to the people she nudged and jostled as she made her way towards the front of the room.

'Sorry, don't mind us,' the man said as he pulled out a chair for the woman.

'I can manage,' she told him, as she sat beside Agent Ratner. 'Hi there, what's good to eat here?'

'Won't be a minute,' the man called. He sat down on the other side of Ratner. 'You eating that?' he asked.

Ratner just stared at him.

'Shame to see it wasted,' the woman said, and pulled Ratner's plate in front of her. 'Donna,' she said, through a mouthful of jeranga fruit. 'This is good.'

The man leaned across and scooped up a few chunks of fruit with his fingers. 'The Doctor. Don't mind us.' he raised his voice to call to Antelect. 'Okey dokey – ready when you are.'

'I see the cabaret has arrived early,' Antelect said drily. The audience chuckled politely.

Then burst into laughter as the man – the Doctor – turned round as if looking eagerly to see where the cabaret might be.

But the strange man's antics were soon forgotten as Antelect got into his act. He started with a top hat, from which he pulled a bunch of flowers that Ood Delta had placed inside earlier. Then Antelect lowered the flowers carefully back into the hat, and pulled them out again. Only now they were a bunny rabbit he was holding by its ears.

The audience gasped and clapped. The bunny grinned and giggled.

'Oh, that is so clever,' the Doctor enthused loudly.

'Bravo,' the woman, Donna, called.

Antelect ignored them. He asked for a volunteer, and managed to pick a young lady who was not Donna to come up on the stage. And with a clap of his hands he made her vanish.

'Can you see yourself?' he asked the lady.

'No,' she gasped. 'I hold up my hand – and it isn't there.'

She faded back into existence, and the audience clapped.

'Off you go then,' Antelect told her. 'But be careful not to lose your head.' With an audible pop, the lady's head disappeared.

Several people actually stood up at that – the Doctor clapping as loudly as any of them. 'Ooh, look,' he announced.

'Her arms have gone too.'

And they had.

Antelect's mouth dropped open. How did that happen? He looked at Ood Delta standing silently at the side of the stage. The Ood's eyes were glowing a faint red, but that was normal. That was how the trick worked.

'And back again!' the Doctor said.

The lady's head and arms were back. The audience was clapping. Antelect was staring at the Doctor. And the Doctor was staring back at him.

Move on, move on, Antelect thought to himself. Now for the most important part of the show. He had already researched the audience, checked out the guests, and knew who he needed for the next part of the act.

'Lady Delatron,' he said, 'if you are here, would you please come to the stage.'

There was polite applause for the third richest woman in the cosmos. The former simularity-star and chart show host made her elegant way to the stage. Antelect smiled in greeting. He glanced at her aristocratic beauty, her pale features, her perfectly sculpted white hair. He stared greedily at the famous Gangestic Necklace with its perfect crystalline nectar-stone set in diamonds and oolian.

And as he stared at it, he imagined it wasn't there. He imagined it was in the safe in Lady Delatron's hotel room.

It worked just as the rest of the act worked. Antelect's thoughts, his imaginings, were picked up by Ood Delta and relayed by telepathy to the audience. What Antelect imagined, the audience saw. If he imagined a bunch of flowers became a rabbit, then it did. If he imagined a woman was invisible, then the audience simply could not see her. Even Antelect himself was affected.

So he had to remember the exact placement of the necklace,

so he could easily remove it while imagining that it was not there, and that he himself was on the other side of the stage, never going anywhere near Lady Delatron as she helped him with a simple card trick. Afterwards, she would swear that the necklace had been in the safe in her room. So that was where it must have been stolen from, while Antelect was performing in front of a hundred witnesses, including Agent Ratner. The perfect alibi, Antelect thought as he removed the necklace and slipped it into his pocket.

'Ladies and gentlemen,' Antelect said, holding up the pack of cards. 'We are honoured tonight to have with us Special Agent Ratner of the Galactic Enforcement Agency who is investigating a series of clever and despicable thefts from top hotels in this sector.'

Hang on – that wasn't what Antelect was saying. But it was what he heard. What the audience heard.

'And I am delighted that this evening,' Antelect heard himself continue, 'I shall be able to explain exactly how the thefts were carried out, and name the culprit.'

No!

Antelect struggled to imagine himself doing the card trick. He was doing the card trick. But someone else – someone with a more powerful imagination, a more powerful grasp on Ood Delta's telepathic abilities had taken control. He saw himself holding up the pack of cards. And he saw the pack of cards turn into Lady Delatron's priceless necklace.

'It was me,' Antelect said calmly. 'And this is how I did it...'

Two massive Kalrusian security dogs stood either side of Antelect. For the first time in as long as he could remember, Agent Ratner was enjoying his evening. The ballroom was empty now apart from Ratner and his prisoner, the security team, Ood Delta, and the two people who had joined Ratner for dinner.

'I've seen it happen before,' Ratner said with evident satisfaction. He poured himself some wine. 'A criminal thinks he is just so clever he needs appreciation. He needs to tell someone how it's done.'

'But I didn't,' Antelect protested. 'I didn't confess.'

'I saw you,' Donna said. 'We all saw you. I liked the bit with the bunny,' she added.

The Doctor just smiled.

'It was a trick,' Antelect insisted.

'Oh I know,' Donna agreed. 'But it was impressive though.'

'No, not the rabbit thing. When I confessed – I didn't.'

Ratner laughed. 'You're seriously expecting us to believe that you didn't actually stand up there and tell us how it was done? How you reset the chronometers with a remote digitiser so the act started later than everyone thought, giving you time to break into the rooms and steal the valuables?'

'But that isn't how it was done!'

'Oh?' said the Doctor. 'So you do know how it was done then?'

'No, I – ' Antelect sighed. 'Ood Delta can tell you. I didn't manipulate the chronometers or anything like that. I'm innocent. An Ood can't lie – ask him!'

Furiously, Antelect imagined himself innocent. They had to believe he hadn't done it, but he couldn't tell them someone was manipulating their minds and making them see things that weren't true – not without giving himself away.

Ood Delta's eyes were a dull red as Antelect's influence took hold.

'So tell us, Ood Delta,' Ratner said. 'This is a serious allegation. Has someone set up Mr Antelect here? Or did he change the clocks?'

'Yes,' the Doctor said quietly. 'Do tell. In your own time, and in your own words. Tell us what you want to say.' He leaned forward across the table, watching Ood Delta intently. 'Is Antelect telling the truth? Is he being framed?'

The red glow faded from the Ood's eyes. 'Mr Antelect is telling the truth,' Ood Delta said.

'Come off it,' Donna said.

'He did not use a digitiser or change the clocks.'

Antelect said nothing. He closed his eyes, thankful that the Ood was so literal and had simply answered the question. He hadn't treated Ood Delta very well, he realised. Maybe in

future, Antelect would be a bit more sensitive, a bit kinder. But then again, he was just an Ood.

'To answer your second question, technically, he is not being framed,' Ood Delta went on.

'That's enough,' Antelect snapped. 'You've answered the questions. Now I demand to be released.'

But Ood Delta was not finished. 'Mister Fergus Antelect is indeed guilty of thirty-seven counts of theft, ninety-two counts of misleading the public through illegal telepathic manipulation, and one hundred and thirteen counts of cruelty to a sentient life form – namely Ood Delta.'

Antelect gave a nervous laugh. 'Oh, you can't possibly prove that.'

'But Ood Delta can remember it,' the Doctor said quietly. 'Can't you?'

Ood Delta's eyes glowed the faintest red as his thoughts, his memories – memories of what actually happened during each of Antelect's performances – were transmitted into the minds of everyone there.

'You might have fooled the audiences,' Ratner said as he realised what had really happened. 'With a hundred or more witnesses there was never any point in checking the hotel's security videos for the shows. But now, well, I think they might tell a very different story, don't you?'

Antelect yelled and struggled, but the Kalrusians held him tight. 'I'd have gotten away with it if it weren't for that meddling Doctor and his friend,' he raged.

'Quite possibly,' Agent Ratner agreed. He turned to thank the Doctor and Donna, to ask them who they were and where they had come from.

But the chairs beside him were empty. It was as if the two of them had vanished into thin air.

DOCTOR · WHO

OTHER GREAT FILES TO COLLECT

1. The Doctor
2. Rose
3. The Slitheen
4. The Sycorax
5. Mickey
6. K-9
7. The Daleks
8. The Cybermen
9. Martha
10. Captain Jack
11. The Cult of Skaro
12. The TARDIS
13. The Sontarans
14. The Ood